Contents

GW00864263

A **pull-out answers section** (pages A1 to A8) appears in the centre of this book, between pages 20 and 21. It also gives simple guidance on how best to use this book. Remove this section before you begin working through the tests.

■ Underline the two words, **one** from each group, that mean almost the **same**.

> Example (hot, <u>cool</u>, heat)   (sky, day, <u>cold</u>)

1. (quick, run, wait)   (walk, fast, sit)
2. (sound, noisy, radio)   (bang, shout, loud)
3. (jumper, sneeze, cold)   (sunny, chilly, scarf)

■ Choose the word in brackets that will complete the sentence in the best way. Underline the answer.

> Example **Cat** is to **kitten** as **dog** is to (paw, <u>puppy</u>, animal).

4. **Little** is to **mouse** as **enormous** is to (rat, hippopotamus, hamster).
5. **Drive** is to **car** as **ride** is to (person, bike, lorry).
6. **Father** is to **man** as **mother** is to (sister, woman, kind).

■ Underline the two words, **one** from each group, that are most **opposite** in meaning.

> Example (<u>large</u>, down, in)   (<u>tiny</u>, tree, hat)

7. (big, up, round)   (small, horse, hill)
8. (day, early, sun)   (sleep, night, bed)
9. (house, in, door)   (shop, out, about)

■ Underline the word that goes best with the three words in brackets.

> Example (bonnet, cap, beanie)   <u>hat</u>, coat, shoes

10. (car, van, lorry)   boat, train, truck
11. (star, triangle, square)   circle, clown, tree
12. (high, above, raised)   up, down, below

End of test.

Score:	Time taken:	Target met?

Target time: **12 minutes**

1–3. For each of the words below, choose the correct group. Write its letter on the line.

A = animal **I** = insect

deer _____   beetle _____   rabbit _____

tiger _____   bee _____   fly _____

In each group, three words go together and one is the odd one out. Underline the word that does **not** go with the other three.

Example   one   two   <u>out</u>   six

4. cat   dog   sun   mouse
5. blue   purple   yellow   door
6. duck   monkey   swan   seagull

Underline the two words, **one** from each group, that are most **opposite** in meaning.

Example   (<u>big</u>, up, round)   (<u>small</u>, elephant, house)

7. (roof, man, high)   (mat, garden, low)
8. (top, shoe, stairs)   (table, bottom, rest)
9. (press, open, play)   (shut, cry, put)

Two words in each sentence must change places so that the sentence makes sense. Underline the two words.

Example   Where do you <u>to</u> go school?   (Where do you <u>go</u> to school?)

10. How are old you?
11. Is what your name?
12. Where do live you?

End of test.

Score:		Time taken:		Target met?	

■ Underline the pair of words that mean almost the **same**.

> Example (hot, cool)   (freezing, sunny)   (cool, cold)

1. (box, door)   (shut, close)   (window, lid)
2. (lose, look)   (angry, cross)   (frown, blink)
3. (dream, better)   (sleep, food)   (sick, ill)

■ Choose the word in brackets that will complete the sentence in the best way. Underline the answer.

> Example **Cat** is to **kitten** as **dog** is to (paw, puppy, animal).

4. **Television** is to **watch** as **book** is to (read, eat, play).
5. **Funny** is to **laugh** as **sad** is to (smile, cry, blue).
6. **Winter** is to **snowy** as **summer** is to (sunny, icy, holiday).

■ 7–9. For each of the words below, choose the correct group. Write its letter on the line.

> **F** = fruit   **V** = vegetable

apple _____   orange _____   carrot _____

parsnip _____   potato _____   cabbage _____

■ In each group, three words go together and one is the odd one out. Underline the word that does **not** go with the other three.

> Example one   two   out   six

10. library   sand   bucket   spade
11. paw   foot   tail   hoof
12. small   tiny   large   little

End of test.

Score:	Time taken:	Target met?

Target time: **12 minutes**

■ Find the missing letters in each word. Choose from the letters given below. You may only use each letter once. Write the missing letter on the line.

a h o m b e

Example h _a_ t

1. __ in   2. __ ip   3. __ gg

___

■ In each of the sentences below, the word in capitals has three letters missing. Those three letters spell a word. Write the three-letter word in the gap.

Example She left the door O _P_ _E_ _N_.   (OPEN)

4. The M O N __ __ __ ate a banana.

5. Will you P __ __ __ with me?

6. I will S __ __ __ you how it works.

___

■ If these words were listed in alphabetical order, which word would come **first**? Write the answer on the line.

Example dog   cat   vet   sit   cow   ___cat___

7. man   fat   rib   cap   _____

8. dip   mop   ant   boy   _____

9. pan   zoo   you   toe   _____

___

■ Find the missing letter that completes **both** words. Write the letter on the line. Choose your answer from these letters:

l t h

Example tap (_e_) at   (tape and eat)

10. wis (__) ope   11. boo (__) ent   12. rea (__) ick

End of test.

Score:		Time taken:		Target met?	

⬇
■ In each of the sentences below, the word in capitals has three letters missing. Those three letters spell a word. Write the three-letter word in the gap.

> **Example** She left the door O P E N .   (OPEN)

1. I paid the B __ __ __.

2. He lit the fire with a __ __ __ C H .

3. The little boy fell D __ __ __.

■ Find the **three-letter word** hidden in each longer word. You will not need to change the letter order. Underline the word and write it on the line.

> **Example** lathe ___the___

4. ripple   _____

5. thrill   _____

6. dear   _____

■ Underline the **two** words that contain all the same letters.

> **Example** two   now   was   won   you

7. tea   get   ear   let   are

8. who   yaw   tow   way   tag

9. wow   woe   how   eye   who

■ Underline the two words, **one** from each group, that together make one new word. The word from the first group comes first.

> **Example** (foot, head, face)   (shoe, ball, mask)   (football)

10. (circle, round, oval)   (under, about, in)

11. (gold, ice, water)   (ring, pot, fish)

12. (cow, milk, dairy)   (shake, glass, farm)

End of test.

Score:	Time taken:	Target met?

Target time: **12 minutes**

■ Change the first word into the last word. Only change **one** letter at a time. You must make a new word in the middle. Write the new word on the line.

Example MAN [__PAN__] PIN

1. TOP [_____] NIP
2. PAT [_____] POP
3. SIT [_____] SAG

■ In each of the sentences below, the word in capitals has three letters missing. Those three letters spell a word. Write the three-letter word in the gap.

Example She left the door O P E N .   (OPEN)

4. I did not want to S __ __ __ playing on the swings.
5. The little girl had fun at the BIRTH __ __ __ party.
6. We played FOOTB __ __ __ together.

■ Underline the two words, **one** from each group, that together make one new word. The word from the first group comes first.

Example (foot, head, face)   (shoe, ball, mask)   (football)

7. (house, pan, cook)   (cake, heat, cookie)
8. (bread, butter, cheese)   (run, fly, jump)
9. (group, class, learn)   (house, room, teach)

■ If these words were listed in alphabetical order, which word would come **last**? Write the answer on the line.

Example dog   cat   vet   sit   cow   ___vet___

10. sky   try   rot   lop   _____
11. go   now   the   sip   _____
12. mat   hip   dot   fan   _____

End of test.

Score:		Time taken:		Target met?	

Target time: **12 minutes**

↓
■ Find the next number in the sequence. Write it on the line.

Example   14   15   16   17   18   __19__   (+1 each time)

1. 6   7   8   9   10   _____

2. 3   4   5   6   7   _____

3. 13   14   15   16   17   _____

■ Use the information given to answer the sum. Write your answer as a **letter**.

Example   A = 1   B = 2   C = 3   D = 5   **A + B =** __C__   (1 + 2 = 3)

4. A = 5   B = 7   C = 13   D = 12   **A + B =** _____

5. A = 17   B = 9   C = 14   D = 8   **D + B =** _____

6. A = 5   B = 11   C = 16   D = 12   **B + A =** _____

■ Work out the missing number. Write it on the line.

Example   3 [5] 2   4 [6] 2   5 [__8__] 3
(a + b = ?, where a is the number on the left and b is the number on the right)

7. 14 [15] 1   13 [15] 2   12 [_____] 3

8. 4 [3] 1   5 [4] 1   6 [_____] 1

9. 3 [10] 7   4 [10] 6   1 [_____] 9

■ Find the missing number in each equation. Write it on the line.

Example   1 + 3 = 2 + __2__   (1 + 3 = 4 and so does 2 + 2)

10. 4 − 1 = 5 − _____

11. 5 + 1 = 3 + _____

12. 10 − 7 = 2 + _____

End of test.

Score:	Time taken:	Target met?

Target time: **12 minutes**

■ Work out the missing number. Write it on the line.

Example 3 [5] 2   4 [6] 2   5 [___8___] 3
(a + b = ?, where a is the number on the left and b is the number on the right)

1. 7 [9] 2   8 [12] 4   5 [_____] 10
2. 3 [16] 13   14 [26] 12   15 [_____] 1
3. 15 [2] 13   16 [12] 4   7 [_____] 2

■ Find the missing number in each equation. Write it on the line.

Example 1 + 3 = 2 + ___2___   (1 + 3 = 4 and so does 2 + 2)

4. 16 + 3 = 9 + _____
5. 40 – 30 = 1 + _____
6. 2 + 3 = 5 + _____

■ Find the next number in the sequence. Write it on the line.

Example 14   15   16   17   18   ___19___   (+1 each time)

7. 27   28   29   30   31   _____
8. 47   46   45   44   43   _____
9. 3   5   7   9   11   _____

■ Use the information given to answer the sum. Write your answer as a **letter**.

Example A = 1   B = 2   C = 3   D = 5   **A + B =** ___C___   (1 + 2 = 3)

10. A = 3   B = 6   C = 6   D = 9   **A + C =** _____
11. A = 11   B = 4   C = 6   D = 7   **D + B =** _____
12. A = 9   B = 15   C = 8   D = 6   **B – D =** _____

End of test.

Score:	Time taken:	Target met?

⬇ Find the next letter in the sequence. Use the alphabet to help you. Write the letter on the line.

A B C D E F G H I J K L M N O P Q R S T U V W X Y Z

Example A B C D E __F__   (+1 each time)

1. L M N O P ____

2. T S R Q P ____

3. D G D G D ____

Find the letter that completes each sentence. Use the alphabet to help you. Write the letter on the line.

A B C D E F G H I J K L M N O P Q R S T U V W X Y Z

Example **A** is to **B** as **D** is to __E__ .   (+1 each time)

4. **L** is to **K** as **E** is to _____ .

5. **P** is to **S** as **H** is to _____ .

6. **N** is to **P** as **B** is to _____ .

Make a new word. Change the third pair of words in the same way as the other pairs. Write the new word on the line.

Example (mat, at)   (fit, it)   (son, ___on___)   (take away the first letter of the first word)

7. (pop, pope)   (mop, mope)   (hop, _____)

8. (mane, man)   (vane, van)   (pane, _____)

9. (hat, hate)   (rat, rate)   (mat, _____)

Match the number codes to the words. Use this to help you work out the answers to the questions. Write your answers on the lines.

TOE   ONE   TAN   153   413   465

10. What is the code for **TAN**? _____

11. What is the code for **TOE**? _____

12. What does the code **153** mean? _____

End of test.

Score:		Time taken:		Target met?	

Target time: **15 minutes**

■ Find the code. Use the alphabet to help you. Write the code on the line.

A B C D E F G H I J K L M N O P Q R S T U V W X Y Z

Example If the code for **TOP** is **UPQ**, what is the code for **TIP**? ___UJQ___ (+1 each time)

1. If the code for **TOP** is **UPQ**, what is the code for **POT**? _____

2. If the code for **HIT** is **IJU**, what is the code for **END**? _____

3. If the code for **NOT** is **OPU**, what is the code for **BOY**? _____

■ Match the number codes to the words. Use this to help you work out the answers to the questions. Write your answers on the lines.

USE SET SUN 174 135 713

4. What is the code for **SET**? _____

5. What is the code for **SUN**? _____

6. What does the code **713** mean? _____

■ The word in square brackets has been made by some of the letters from the two outside words. Make a new word in the middle of the second group of words in the same way. Write the new word on the line.

Example (toe [tap] rap) (low [___lit___] sit)

7. (bus [bat] cat) (sun [_____] mat)

8. (ran [ant] tip) (lit [_____] sap)

9. (toe [tap] lap) (bat [_____] run)

■ Find the next letter in the sequence. Use the alphabet to help you. Write the letter on the line.

A B C D E F G H I J K L M N O P Q R S T U V W X Y Z

Example A B C D E ___F___ (+1 each time)

10. R S R S R ___   11. V W V W V ___   12. T U V W X ___

End of test.

Score:		Time taken:		Target met?	

⬇
■ Read the following information. Work out the answers. Write your answers on the lines.

1. James is having a race with 2 of his friends. James does not win the race but he does not come last either. In what place did James finish the race? _____

2. Three people are standing in a line. Shameet is first in the line. Sally is second in the line. Sally is standing in front of Greg. Where is Greg in the line? _____

3. Jack has 11 books. He gives 6 books to his friend. How many books does Jack have left? _____

4. Sam has 7 t-shirts. 3 are red and the rest are yellow. How many yellow t-shirts does Sam have? _____

■ Circle the letter next to the **true** statement for each question.

5. An apple is a type of fruit. All fruits contain seeds.

   If the above statements are true, which one of the following statements must also be true?
   A. All apples are green.
   B. Apples contain seeds.
   C. Horses eat apples.

6. Jon always wears brown shoes on Tuesdays. It is Tuesday today.

   If the above statements are true, which one of the following statements must also be true?
   A. Jon likes shoes.
   B. Jon's shoes have shoelaces.
   C. Jon is wearing brown shoes today.

■ Read the following questions. Work out the answers. Write your answers on the lines.

7. How many days in a week? _____

8. How many months in a year? _____

9. Which day comes after Monday? _____

10. Which month comes after February? _____

11. What is the day before Sunday? _____

12. Which day comes before Saturday? _____

End of test.

Score:		Time taken:		Target met?	

Target time: 15 minutes

■ Read the following information. Work out the answers. Write your answers on the lines.

1. I have a bowl of 8 plums.
   If I share them equally with my sister, how many plums will we each have?
   _____

2. It is 5 o'clock now. What time will it be in 2 hours? _____

3. The postman is delivering letters.
   He goes to Lily's house first then to Daisy's house.
   Next he goes to Holly's house. He goes to Ben's house last.
   Whose house does he go to second? _____

4. My mother is making phone calls.
   She calls my gran first.
   Next she calls my uncle and then she calls my aunt.
   Lastly she calls my gran again.
   Who does my mother call third? _____

5. Lizzie has 5 cats.
   2 have pink collars, 1 has a blue collar and the rest have white collars.
   How many blue and pink collars are there altogether? _____

6. Gita is decorating some cupcakes.
   6 have sprinkles on top, 3 have white icing and 3 have pink icing.
   The ones with the sprinkles on have yellow icing.
   How many cupcakes have yellow icing? _____

■ Fill in the blanks.

7. Wednesday Thursday _____ Saturday

8. Sunday Monday Tuesday _____ Thursday

9. spring summer _____ winter

10. Monday Tuesday Wednesday _____ Friday

11. January February March _____ May

12. March April May June _____

End of test.

Score:	Time taken:	Target met?

⬇
■ Read the following information. Work out the answers. Write your answers on the lines.

1. Zoe is eating a packet of sweets. Half of them have pink wrappers, 4 have yellow wrappers and 2 have green wrappers. There are 12 sweets altogether.
   How many have pink wrappers? _____

2. Jake's pet tabby cat has 5 kittens. 3 are black, 1 is white and the other is a tabby.
   How many tabby cats are there altogether? _____

3. Zak and his friends are eating crisps. Alan and Mick have salt and vinegar, Zak has cheese and onion, and Stephen and Jo have sweet chilli.
   How many children are there altogether? _____

■ Circle the letter next to the **true** statement for each question.

4. Rishi only eats strawberry ice-cream. Strawberry ice-cream is pink.

   If the above statements are true, which one of the following statements must also be true?
   A. Rishi only eats pink ice-cream.   B. Ice-cream tastes nice.   C. Sally wants some ice-cream.

5. A car has an engine. Engines need fuel to run.

   If the above statements are true, which one of the following statements must also be true?
   A. Cars need fuel to run.   B. Petrol is a type of fuel.   C. Garages sell petrol.

6. A hen is a type of bird. All birds lay eggs.

   If the above statements are true, which one of the following statements must also be true?
   A. Eggs have a yolk inside.   B. It is hard to break an egg.   C. Hens lay eggs.

■ Read the following questions. Work out the answers. Write your answers on the lines.

7. How many days are there in 2 weeks? _____

8. How many months are there in 2 years? _____

9. Amy is 5 now. How old will she be on her next birthday? _____

10. Kamil is 6 now. How old will he be on his next birthday? _____

11. What is the date on the day before 23 March? _____

12. What date is the day after 28 December? _____

End of test.

Score:		Time taken:		Target met?	

Target time: **12 minutes**

Underline the word in brackets that is **closest** in meaning to the word in capitals.

Example HUGE (mouse, large, elephant, small)

1. SAD (mat, house, room, unhappy)
2. TIRED (old, late, sleepy, nap)
3. CHOOSE (root, lock, table, pick)
4. GOOD (land, carpet, sheet, fine)

Choose the word in brackets that will complete the sentence in the best way. Underline the answer.

Example **Cat** is to **kitten** as **dog** is to (paw, puppy, animal).

5. **Kind** is to **nice** as **mean** is to (tell, sort, nasty).
6. **Cup** is to **drink** as **plate** is to (eat, round, water).
7. **Lie** is to **bed** as **sit** is to (shelf, chair, window).
8. **Dog** is to **growl** as **lion** is to (squeak, giggle, roar).

Underline the word in brackets that is **opposite** in meaning to the word in capitals.

Example SMALL (mouse, large, elephant, small)

9. DARK (night, black, door, light)
10. COLD (drink, winter, sunny, hot)
11. STOP (red, car, go, run)

Read the following information. Work out the answer. Write your answer on the line.

12. There are 28 children in Sam's class. 16 of them are girls.
How many are boys? _____

End of test.

Score:	Time taken:	Target met?

⬇

■ **1–4.** For each of the words below, choose the correct group. Write its letter on the line.

C = colour F = flower

blue _____   daisy _____   tulip _____   brown _____

lily _____   green _____   daffodil _____   white _____

■ In each group, three words go together and one is the odd one out. Underline the word that does **not** go with the other three.

Example one   two   <u>out</u>   six

5. three   star   one   six

6. strawberry   carrot   banana   cherry

7. kind   mean   friendly   nice

8. sofa   chair   table   path

■ Choose the most sensible word to complete each sentence. Underline the word.

Example A **cat** always has (mice, hair, <u>paws</u>).

9. A **fish** always has (fins, stripes, a net).

10. A **plane** always has (passengers, wings, a driver).

11. A **chicken** always has a (chick, nest, beak).

■ Read the following information. Work out the answer. Write your answer on the line.

12. Julie and her friends, Alice and Li, each buy an ice-cream. Li has strawberry and chocolate ice-cream with a flake, Alice has vanilla ice-cream with two flakes and Julie has mint ice-cream with no flakes.
How many children have flakes in their ice-creams? _____

End of test.

Score:		Time taken:		Target met?	

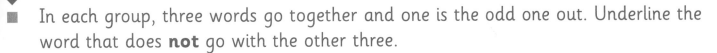
Target time: **12 minutes**

In each group, three words go together and one is the odd one out. Underline the word that does **not** go with the other three.

Example one   two   <u>out</u>   six

1. flower   building   bush   tree
2. dance   sleep   nap   rest
3. magazine   book   television   newspaper
4. dinner   lunch   breakfast   yesterday

Choose the word in brackets that will complete the sentence in the best way. Underline the answer.

Example **Cat** is to **kitten** as **dog** is to (paw, <u>puppy</u>, animal).

5. **Feet** are to **socks** as **hands** are to (coat, trousers, gloves).
6. **Drum** is to **hit** as **whistle** is to (throw, blow, happy).
7. **Light** is to **dark** as **high** is to (low, under, away).
8. **Cat** is to **furry** as **hedgehog** is to (night, cute, prickly).

Underline the two words, **one** from each group, that mean almost the **same**.

Example (hot, <u>cool</u>, heat)   (sky, day, <u>cold</u>)

9. (funny, laugh, joke)   (giggle, poke, clown)
10. (top, fight, bad)   (evil, hill, grass)
11. (smile, coat, wear)   (grin, clap, shoes)

Circle the letter next to the **true** statement.

12.   A snowdrop is a type of flower. All flowers have petals.

   If the above statements are true, which one of the following statements must also be true?
   A. Snowdrops grow from bulbs.
   B. Snowdrops have petals.
   C. All white flowers grow in winter.

End of test.

Score:		Time taken:		Target met?	

⬇

■ Remove **one** letter from each word to make a new, correctly spelt word. Write the new word on the line.

Example trip ____rip____ (remove the t)

1. cup _____

2. gown _____

3. seen _____

4. skunk _____

■ In each of the sentences below, the word in capitals has three letters missing. Those three letters spell a word. Write the three-letter word in the gap.

Example She left the door O _P_ _E_ _N_ . (OPEN)

5. We saw cows, chickens and horses at the __ __ __ M.

6. Do you K __ __ __ my name?

7. I hope that the rain will go A __ __ __ later.

8. It is Sunday T O __ __ __.

■ Rearrange the word in capitals. Use the letters to make another word that goes with the first two. Write the new word on the line.

Example arm finger GEL ____LEG____

9. sleep rest PAN _____

10. pan container TOP _____

11. eye nose ARE _____

■ Read the following information. Work out the answer. Write your answer on the line.

12. Ellie is in the supermarket queue. There are two people in front of her and three behind her. What position is Ellie in the queue? _____

End of test.

Score:		Time taken:		Target met?	

Notes for parents, tutors, teachers and other adult helpers

- **Verbal Reasoning 1** is designed for six- and seven-year-olds, but may also be suitable for some older children.

- Remove this pull-out section before giving the book to the child.

- Before the child begins work on the first test, read together the instructions on page 2, headed **What to do**. As you do so, look together at **Section 1 Test 1** and point out to the child the different elements.

- As each question type is introduced for the first time within a particular test, an example is given. Where question types recur throughout the book, the same example is provided. This is deliberate: the example will act as a useful reminder, but children will not need to work through it repeatedly from scratch.

- Make sure that the child understands how to answer the questions and that he or she has a pencil and eraser. You should also ensure that the child is able to see a clock or a watch.

- Be sure that the child knows to tell you clearly when he or she has finished the test.

- When the child is ready, say 'Start the test now' and make a note of the start time.

- When the child has finished, work out how long he or she took to complete the test. Then fill in the **Time taken** box, which appears at the end of the test.

- Mark the child's work using this pull-out section, giving one mark for each correct answer unless instructed otherwise. Then complete the **Score** box at the end of the test.

- The table below shows you how to mark the **Target met?** box and the **Action** notes help you to plan the next step. However, these are suggestions only. Please use your own judgement as you decide how best to proceed.

Score	Time taken*	Target met?	Action
1–6	Any	Not yet	Provide help and support as needed.
7–9	Any	Not yet	Encourage the child to keep practising using the tests in this book. The child may need to repeat some tests. If so, wait a few weeks, or the child may simply remember the correct answers. Provide help and support as needed.
10–12	Over target – child took too long	Not yet	
10–12	On target – child took suggested time or less	Yes	Encourage the child to keep practising using further tests in this book, and to move on to the next book when you think this is appropriate.

* The time taken for the tests varies depending on the types of questions included.

- Whatever the test score, always encourage the child to have another go at the questions that he or she got wrong – without looking at the solutions. If the child's answers are still incorrect, work through these questions together. Demonstrate the correct method if necessary.

- If the child struggles with particular question types, help him or her to develop the strategies needed.

The **Understanding Reasoning** series, also available from Schofield & Sims, provides clear explanations on how to answer reasoning questions. It also provides 'Tips for tests' and 'Tips for revision'. For further details on this and other series that help children and young people to prepare for school selection tests, and for free downloads relating to the **Rapid Reasoning Tests**, visit www.schofieldandsims.co.uk

Answers

Section 1 Test 1 (page 4)

1. quick, fast
2. noisy, loud
3. cold, chilly
4. hippopotamus
5. bike
6. woman
7. big, small
8. day, night
9. in, out
10. truck
11. circle
12. up

Section 1 Test 2 (page 5)

1–3. *[score half a point for each correct answer]* deer = A, beetle = I, rabbit = A, tiger = A, bee = I, fly = I
4. sun (the others are all animals)
5. door (the rest are colours)
6. monkey (the others are all birds)
7. high, low
8. top, bottom
9. open, shut
10. are old (How <u>old</u> <u>are</u> you?)
11. Is what (<u>What</u> <u>is</u> your name?)
12. live you (Where do <u>you</u> <u>live</u>?)

Section 1 Test 3 (page 6)

1. shut, close
2. angry, cross
3. sick, ill
4. read
5. cry
6. sunny
7–9. *[score half a point for each correct answer]* apple = F, orange = F, carrot = V, parsnip = V, potato = V, cabbage = V
10. library (the others are to do with the beach)
11. tail (the rest are to do with feet)
12. large (the other words all mean small)

Section 1 Test 4 (page 7)

1. b (bin)
2. h (hip)
3. e (egg)
4. KEY (MONKEY)
5. LAY (PLAY)
6. HOW (SHOW)
7. cap
8. ant
9. pan
10. h (wish and hope)
11. t (boot and tent)
12. l (real and lick)

Section 1 Test 5 (page 8)

1. ILL (BILL)
2. MAT (MATCH)
3. OWN (DOWN)
4. r<u>ipp</u>le   rip
5. th<u>rill</u>   ill
6. d<u>ear</u>   ear
7. ear, are
8. yaw, way
9. how, who
10. roundabout
11. goldfish
12. milkshake

Section 1 Test 6 (page 9)

1. TOP [<u>TIP</u>] NIP
2. PAT [<u>POT</u>] POP
3. SIT [<u>SAT</u>] SAG
4. TOP (STOP)
5. DAY (BIRTHDAY)
6. ALL (FOOTBALL)
7. pancake
8. butterfly
9. classroom
10. try
11. the
12. mat

Section 1 Test 7 (page 10)
1. 11 (+1)
2. 8 (+1)
3. 18 (+1)
4. D (5 + 7 = 12)
5. A (8 + 9 = 17)
6. C (11 + 5 = 16)
7. 15 (a + b)
8. 5 (a − b)
9. 10 (a + b)
10. 2
11. 3
12. 1

Section 1 Test 8 (page 11)
1. 15 (a + b)
2. 16 (a + b)
3. 5 (a − b)
4. 10
5. 9
6. 0
7. 32 (+1)
8. 42 (−1)
9. 13 (+2)
10. D (3 + 6 = 9)
11. A (7 + 4 = 11)
12. A (15 − 6 = 9)

Section 1 Test 9 (page 12)
1. Q (+1)
2. O (−1)
3. G (repeating pattern)
4. D (−1)
5. K (+3)
6. D (+2)
7. hope
8. pan
9. mate
10. 465
11. 413
12. ONE

Section 1 Test 10 (page 13)
1. QPU (+1)
2. FOE (+1)
3. CPZ (+1)
4. 135
5. 174
6. USE
7. sat
8. its
9. bun
10. S (repeating pattern)
11. W (repeating pattern)
12. Y (+1)

Section 1 Test 11 (page 14)
1. second (accept 'middle')
2. third (accept 'last')
3. 5
4. 4
5. B
6. C
7. 7
8. 12
9. Tuesday
10. March
11. Saturday
12. Friday

Section 1 Test 12 (page 15)
1. 4
2. 7 o'clock (accept variations)
3. Daisy's house
4. my aunt
5. 3
6. 6
7. Friday
8. Wednesday
9. autumn
10. Thursday
11. April
12. July

Answers

■ Section 2 Test 1 (page 16)

1. 6
2. 2 (mother cat and 1 kitten)
3. 5
4. A
5. A
6. C
7. 14
8. 24
9. 6
10. 7
11. 22 March
12. 29 December

■ Section 2 Test 2 (page 17)

1. unhappy
2. sleepy
3. pick
4. fine
5. nasty
6. eat
7. chair
8. roar
9. light
10. hot
11. go
12. 12

■ Section 2 Test 3 (page 18)

1–4. [score half a point for each correct answer] blue = C, daisy = F, tulip = F, brown = C, lily = F, green = C, daffodil = F, white = C
5. star (the others are numbers)
6. carrot (the others are fruits)
7. mean (the others describe a nice person)
8. path (the rest are furniture)
9. fins
10. wings
11. beak
12. 2

■ Section 2 Test 4 (page 19)

1. building (the others are all plants)
2. dance (the others describe resting)
3. television (you read all the others)
4. yesterday (the rest are meals)
5. gloves
6. blow
7. low
8. prickly
9. laugh, giggle
10. bad, evil
11. smile, grin
12. B

■ Section 2 Test 5 (page 20)

1. up (remove c)
2. own (remove g)
3. see (remove n)
4. sunk (remove k)
5. FAR (FARM)
6. NOW (KNOW)
7. WAY (AWAY)
8. DAY (TODAY)
9. NAP
10. POT
11. EAR
12. third

■ Section 2 Test 6 (page 21)

1. G I N S
2. G
3. A P R T Y
4. P
5. MOW [COW] COT
6. LIE [TIE] TIN
7. LAG [BAG] BIG
8. BIN [BAN] CAN
9. seaside
10. sunlight
11. hosepipe
12. 16

Section 2 Test 7 (page 22)

1. <u>what</u> hat
2. <u>asked</u> ask
3. <u>lone</u> one
4. <u>fragile</u> rag
5. n (bean and nice)
6. p (trip and push)
7. k (pick and kite)
8. starfish
9. sandpit
10. flowerpot
11. postbox
12. 3

Section 2 Test 8 (page 23)

1. 12 (+2)
2. 32 (+2)
3. 50 (+10)
4. 50 (−10)
5. B (18 − 9 = 9)
6. D (9 + 11 = 20)
7. C (15 − 3 = 12)
8. D (7 + 6 = 13)
9. 18 (a + b)
10. 11 (a + b)
11. 10 (a + b)
12. Lin

Section 2 Test 9 (page 24)

1. 1
2. 1
3. 8
4. 10
5. 45 (+1)
6. 1 (repeating pattern)
7. 20 (counting forwards in 5s)
8. 14 (−1)
9. B (20 − 13 = 7)
10. D (15 − 8 = 7)
11. C (10 − 8 = 2)
12. 14

Section 2 Test 10 (page 25)

1. 5 (a × b)
2. 13 (a + b)
3. 4 (a ÷ b)
4. 11 (a + b)
5. 1
6. 3
7. 7
8. C (3 + 18 = 21)
9. A (22 − 12 = 10)
10. B (13 + 14 = 27)
11. C (18 − 7 + 11)
12. C

Section 2 Test 11 (page 26)

1. lot
2. pan
3. hop
4. loot
5. 251
6. 283
7. 281
8. PEA
9. K (+1)
10. I (+1)
11. M (repeating pattern)
12. 30 minutes or half an hour

Section 2 Test 12 (page 27)

1. tool
2. soup
3. top
4. sir
5. LHRR (−1)
6. QNV (−1)
7. MNV (−1)
8. TRD (−1)
9. H (−1)
10. N (+3)
11. Z (+1)
12. 20

Answers

Section 3 Test 1 (page 28)

1–4. *[score half a point for each correct answer]* rectangle = A, bowl = B, cup = B, fork = B, knife = B, kite = A, circle = A, hexagon = A
5. 15 (+3)
6. 5 (repeating pattern)
7. *** (alternate symbols increase by one each time)
8. 27 (–1)
9. eyeball
10. skateboard
11. handstand
12. second (accept 'middle')

Section 3 Test 2 (page 29)

1. 8 (a – b)
2. 19 (a – b)
3. 15 (a – b)
4. 18 (a × b)
5. RUN
6. WET
7. FUN
8. ODD
9. TIE (TIED)
10. ROW (GROW)
11. NOW (SNOW)
12. A

Section 3 Test 3 (page 30)

1. led (remove s)
2. rink (remove b)
3. rip (remove g)
4. sigh (remove t)
5. 1
6. 8
7. 10
8. 2
9. 863
10. 427
11. TEN
12. third

Section 3 Test 4 (page 31)

1. rub
2. kit
3. rip
4. jug
5. R (–1)
6. N (+3)
7. E (–3)
8. Y (+2)
9. D (30 – 16 = 14)
10. D (12 + 23 = 35)
11. B (10 + 11 = 21)
12. 70p

Section 3 Test 5 (page 32)

1. flowers likes (My mum likes flowers.)
2. in swim (Fish swim in the sea.)
3. roared lion (The lion roared loudly.)
4. bananas eat (Monkeys eat bananas.)
5. l (deal and like)
6. e (knee and elf)
7. t (root and tile)
8. n (lion and next)
9. A (–1)
10. R (+1)
11. Q (–1)
12. the man

Section 3 Test 6 (page 33)

1. D (3 × 6 = 18)
2. C (20 ÷ 10 = 2)
3. D (2 × 6 = 12)
4. B (25 ÷ 5 = 5)
5. BNS (–1)
6. CNS (–1)
7. KHD (–1)
8. taste, flavour
9. rock, stone
10. boat, ship
11. bite, nip
12. 4

Section 3 Test 7 (page 34)

1. stepmother
2. pathway
3. toothbrush
4. downstairs
5. e (rose and eat)
6. n (town and nine)
7. g (big and good)
8. r (door and room)
9. gr<u>eat</u>   eat
10. gr<u>inn</u>ed   inn
11. dr<u>ipp</u>ed   rip
12. 3.45 p.m. or 15:45 or quarter to four

Section 3 Test 8 (page 35)

1. 20 (a − b)
2. 50 (a + b)
3. 15 (a × b)
4. 12 (a − b)
5. good, bad
6. old, young
7. black, white
8. happy, sad
9. WIN [<u>WIG</u>] JIG
10. LOW [<u>LOG</u>] DOG
11. LIE [<u>TIE</u>] TIN
12. B

Section 3 Test 9 (page 36)

1. day
2. slim
3. lop
4. gall
5. cheetah
6. fairy
7. cup
8. run
9. down
10. yellow
11. toy
12. 3

Section 3 Test 10 (page 37)

1. S (−3)
2. W (+2)
3. F (−3)
4. G (+3)
5. night (the others are to do with the weather)
6. short (the others describe how something feels)
7. wet (the others all describe the cold)
8. bag (the others are all something you can write with)
9. K (+2)
10. V (+2)
11. U (+3)
12. £6 or £6.00

Section 3 Test 11 (page 38)

1. messy
2. banana
3. dog
4. pond
5. 95 (−1)
6. ☺ (repeating pattern)
7. £ (repeating pattern)
8. 40 (counting backwards in 5s)
9. wow
10. dog
11. when
12. 6

Section 3 Test 12 (page 39)

1. 3
2. 2
3. 5
4. 2
5. 213
6. 512
7. PAL
8. push, pull
9. boy, girl
10. easy, hard
11. on, off
12. B

This book of answers is a pull-out section from
Rapid Reasoning Tests: Verbal Reasoning 1

Published by Schofield & Sims Ltd,
Dogley Mill, Fenay Bridge, Huddersfield HD8 0NQ, UK
Telephone 01484 607080
www.schofieldandsims.co.uk

First published in 2014
Third Impression 2016

Copyright © Schofield & Sims Ltd, 2014

Author: **Siân Goodspeed**. *Siân Goodspeed has asserted her moral right under the Copyright, Designs and Patents Act, 1988, to be identified as the author of this work.*

British Library Cataloguing in Publication Data. *A catalogue record for this book is available from the British Library.*

Commissioned by **Carolyn Richardson Publishing Services** *(www.publiserve.co.uk)*

Design by **Oxford Designers & Illustrators**
Printed in India by **Multivista Global Pvt. Ltd**

ISBN 978 07217 1238 3

Target time: **12 minutes**

⬛ Answer the questions below. Use the alphabet to help you. Write your answers on the lines.

A B C D E F G H I J K L M N O P Q R S T U V W X Y Z

1–2. Put the letters in the word **SING** into alphabetical order. _____

Which letter is now the **first** letter? _____

3–4. Put the letters in the word **PARTY** into alphabetical order. _____

Which letter is now the **second** letter? _____

⬛ Change the first word into the last word. Only change **one** letter at a time. You must make a new word in the middle. Write the new word on the line.

Example MAN [_____PAN_____] PIN

5. MOW [_____] COT

6. LIE [_____] TIN

7. LAG [_____] BIG

8. BIN [_____] CAN

⬛ Underline the two words, **one** from each group, that together make one new word. The word from the first group comes first.

Example (foot, head, face)   (shoe, ball, mask)   (football)

9. (stream, sea, ocean)   (side, behind, counter)

10. (planet, sun, wind)   (light, heavy, weigh)

11. (hose, rope, rubber)   (tunnel, pipe, garden)

⬛ Read the following information. Work out the answer. Write your answer on the line.

12. Daniel gives half of his toy car collection to his friend, Ola. He gives 8 to Ola. How many cars did Daniel have to begin with? _____

End of test.

Score:	Time taken:	Target met?

⬇

■ Find the **three-letter word** hidden in each longer word. You will not need to change the letter order. Underline the word and write it on the line.

> Example la<u>the</u>   <u>the</u>

1. what   _____

2. asked   _____

3. lone   _____

4. fragile   _____

■ Find the missing letter that completes **both** words. Write the letter on the line. Choose your answer from these letters:

p t k n

> Example tap (_e_) at   (tape and eat)

5. bea (__) ice

6. tri (__) ush

7. pic (__) ite

■ Underline the two words, **one** from each group, that together make one new word. The word from the first group comes first.

> Example (<u>foot</u>, head, face)   (shoe, <u>ball</u>, mask)   (football)

8. (star, sky, cloud)   (sea, fish, fire)

9. (dust, soil, sand)   (pit, mine, dig)

10. (flower, leaf, plants)   (hold, pot, grow)

11. (card, stamp, post)   (fire, box, ladder)

■ Read the following information. Work out the answer. Write your answer on the line.

12. There are 6 puppies in a litter. 2 are brown, 1 is black and the rest are cream. How many cream puppies are there? _____

End of test.

Score:		Time taken:		Target met?	

Target time: **12 minutes**

■ Find the next number in the sequence. Write it on the line.

Example 14   15   16   17   18   ___19___   (+1 each time)

1. 2   4   6   8   10   _____

2. 24   26   28   30   _____

3. 10   20   30   40   _____

4. 100   90   80   70   60   _____

■ Use the information given to answer the sum. Write your answer as a **letter**.

Example A = 1   B = 2   C = 3   D = 5   **A + B =** ___C___   (1 + 2 = 3)

5. A = 18   B = 9   C = 16   D = 13   **A – B =** _____

6. A = 9   B = 10   C = 11   D = 20   **A + C =** _____

7. A = 13   B = 3   C = 12   D = 15   **D – B =** _____

8. A = 12   B = 6   C = 7   D = 13   **C + B =** _____

■ Work out the missing number. Write it on the line.

Example 3 [5] 2   4 [6] 2   5 [___8___] 3
(a + b = ?, where a is the number on the left and b is the number on the right)

9. 2 [13] 11   4 [16] 12   11 [_____] 7

10. 11 [12] 1   12 [15] 3   7 [_____] 4

11. 10 [12] 2   9 [10] 1   8 [_____] 2

■ Read the following information. Work out the answer. Write your answer on the line.

12. Three children are in a sack race. Lin finishes ahead of Tommy and Ivan finishes last. Who is first? _____

End of test.

Score:		Time taken:		Target met?	

■ Find the missing number in each equation. Write it on the line.

> Example 1 + 3 = 2 + ___2___   (1 + 3 = 4 and so does 2 + 2)

1. 8 – 4 = 5 – _____

2. 4 + 7 = 10 + _____

3. 18 – 2 = 8 + _____

4. 11 + 19 = 20 + _____

■ Find the next number in the sequence. Write it on the line.

> Example 14   15   16   17   18   ___19___   (+1 each time)

5. 41   42   43   44   _____

6. 1   0   1   0   _____

7. 5   10   15   _____   25

8. 19   18   17   16   15   _____

■ Use the information given to answer the sum. Write your answer as a **letter**.

> Example A = 1   B = 2   C = 3   D = 5   **A + B =** ___C___   (1 + 2 = 3)

9. A = 20   B = 7   C = 13   D = 8   **A – C =** _____

10. A = 15   B = 14   C = 8   D = 7   **A – C =** _____

11. A = 11   B = 8   C = 2   D = 10   **D – B =** _____

■ Read the following information. Work out the answer. Write your answer on the line.

12. Jamie is 2 years older than Mikail. Mikail is 12. How old is Jamie? _____

End of test.

Score:		Time taken:		Target met?	

Target time: **12 minutes**

■ Work out the missing number. Write it on the line.

> Example 3[5]2   4[6]2   5[__8__]3
> (a + b = ?, where a is the number on the left and b is the number on the right)

1. 2[4]2   3[6]2   5[_____]1

2. 7[15]8   6[14]8   3[_____]10

3. 4[2]2   12[6]2   8[_____]2

4. 8[12]4   9[13]4   7[_____]4

■ Find the missing number in each equation. Write it on the line.

> Example 1 + 3 = 2 + __2__   (1 + 3 = 4 and so does 2 + 2)

5. 12 – 1 = 10 + _____

6. 14 – 8 = 9 – _____

7. 16 – 8 = 1 + _____

■ Use the information given to answer the sum. Write your answer as a **letter**.

> Example A = 1   B = 2   C = 3   D = 5   **A + B =** __C__   (1 + 2 = 3)

8. A = 18   B = 3   C = 21   D = 9   **B + A =** _____

9. A = 10   B = 12   C = 18   D = 22   **D – B =** _____

10. A = 13   B = 27   C = 17   D = 14   **A + D =** _____

11. A = 13   B = 18   C = 11   D = 7   **B – D =** _____

■ Circle the letter next to the **true** statement.

12.   All fish swim in water. Plaice are a type of fish.

   If the above statements are true, which one of the following statements must also be true?
   A. Chips go with fish.
   B. Fish have scales.
   C. Plaice swim in water.

End of test.

Score:		Time taken:		Target met?	

⬇
■ Make a new word. Change the third pair of words in the same way as the other pairs. Write the new word on the line.

Example (mat, at)   (fit, it)   (son, __on__)   (take away the first letter of the first word)

1. (row, rot)   (how, hot)   (low, _____)

2. (men, man)   (ten, tan)   (pen, _____)

3. (shut, hut)   (sham, ham)   (shop, _____)

4. (loop, pool)   (room, moor)   (tool, _____)

■ Match the number codes to the words. Use this to help you work out the answers to the questions. Write your answers on the lines.

    ANT   APE   NAP   825   831   382

5. What is the code for **PET**? _____

6. What is the code for **PAN**? _____

7. What is the code for **PAT**? _____

8. What does the code **258** mean? _____

■ Find the next letter in the sequence. Use the alphabet to help you. Write the letter on the line.

A B C D E F G H I J K L M N O P Q R S T U V W X Y Z

Example A B C D E __F__   (+1 each time)

9. F G H I J ____

10. D E F G H ____

11. L M L M L ____

■ Read the following information. Work out the answer. Write your answer on the line.

12. Ned starts his homework at 5 p.m. He finishes it at 5.30 p.m. How long did it take Ned to do his homework? _____

End of test.

Score:		Time taken:		Target met?	

Target time: **15 minutes**

The word in square brackets has been made by some of the letters from the two outside words. Make a new word in the middle of the second group of words in the same way. Write the new word on the line.

Example (toe [tap] rap)   (low [____lit____] sit)

1. (do [door] ore)   (to [_____] old)

2. (one [onto] too)   (so [_____] up)

3. (ted [ten] nest)   (toll [_____] pen)

4. (out [our] ram)   (sit [_____] rid)

Find the code. Use the alphabet to help you. Write the code on the line.
A B C D E F G H I J K L M N O P Q R S T U V W X Y Z

Example If the code for **TOP** is **UPQ**, what is the code for **TIP**? ___UJQ___ (+1 each time)

5. If the code for **YOU** is **XNT**, what is the code for **MISS**? _____

6. If the code for **TOO** is **SNN**, what is the code for **ROW**? _____

7. If the code for **ONE** is **NMD**, what is the code for **NOW**? _____

8. If the code for **LOT** is **KNS**, what is the code for **USE**? _____

Find the letter that completes each sentence. Use the alphabet to help you. Write the letter on the line.
A B C D E F G H I J K L M N O P Q R S T U V W X Y Z

Example **A** is to **B** as **D** is to ___E_ .   (+1 each time)

9. **G** is to **F** as **I** is to ____ .

10. **U** is to **X** as **K** is to ____ .

11. **D** is to **E** as **Y** is to ____ .

Read the following information. Work out the answer. Write your answer on the line.

12. There are 40 sweets in a pack. Mirjana shares them equally with her friend Stefan. How many sweets does each child have? _____

End of test.

Score:	Time taken:	Target met?

Target time: **12 minutes**

⬇
■ 1–4. Look at these groups. For each of the words below, choose the correct group. Write its letter on the line.

A	**B**
triangle	spoon
square	plate

rectangle _____   bowl _____   cup _____   fork _____

knife _____   kite _____   circle _____   hexagon _____

■ Find the next number or symbol in the sequence. Write it on the line.

Example 14 15 16 17 18 __19__   (+1 each time)

5. 3 6 9 12 _____ 18

6. 2 5 2 5 2 _____ 2

7. ! * !! ** !!! _____

8. 30 29 28 _____ 26

■ Underline the two words, **one** from each group, that together make one new word. The word from the first group comes first.

Example (<u>foot</u>, head, face)   (shoe, <u>ball</u>, mask)   (football)

9. (lip, cheek, eye)   (cricket, basket, ball)

10. (slip, skate, run)   (board, jump, ski)

11. (arm, leg, hand)   (finger, stand, stretch)

■ Read the following information. Work out the answer. Write your answer on the line.

12. Samit is in a race with two of his friends. Josh finishes in front of Samit and Niall comes last. Where does Ethan finish? _____

End of test.

Score:	Time taken:	Target met?

Target time: **12 minutes**

■ Work out the missing number. Write it on the line.

Example 3[5]2   4[6]2   5[___8___]3
(a + b = ?, where a is the number on the left and b is the number on the right)

1. 23[9]14   21[9]12   23[_____]15

2. 17[15]2   19[17]2   21[_____]2

3. 21[7]14   28[14]14   30[_____]15

4. 6[12]2   8[16]2   9[_____]2

■ Rearrange the word in capitals. Use the letters to make a new word. The sentence must make sense. Write the new word on the line.

Example The **NUS** shone brightly. ___SUN___

5. I had to NRU fast to win the race. _____

6. The weather was TWE. _____

7. James went to the NFU fair. _____

8. Three is an DDO number. _____

■ In each of the sentences below, the word in capitals has three letters missing. Those three letters spell a word. Write the three-letter word in the gap.

Example She left the door O P E N . (OPEN)

9. I __ __ __ D my shoelaces.

10. I hope the flower will G __ __ __ very tall.

11. The S __ __ __ was cold and white.

■ Circle the letter next to the **true** statement.

12. Lions are a type of big cat. Big cats hunt for food.

If the above statements are true, which one of the following statements must also be true?
A. Lions hunt for their food.
B. Lions are always hungry.
C. Lions like food.

End of test.

Score:		Time taken:		Target met?	

↓
■ Remove **one** letter from each of the words below to make a new, correctly spelt word. Write the new word on the line.

| Example trip ___rip___ (remove the t) |

1. sled _____
2. brink _____
3. grip _____
4. sight _____

■ Find the missing number in each equation. Write it on the line.

| Example 1 + 3 = 2 + ___2___   (1 + 3 = 4 and so does 2 + 2) |

5. $20 - 7 = 14 -$ _____
6. $19 - 3 = 8 +$ _____
7. $24 - 4 = 10 +$ _____
8. $70 - 9 = 59 +$ _____

■ Match the number codes to the words. Use this to help you work out the answers to the questions. Write your answers on the lines.

BIN   NEW   BET   368   327   824

9. What is the code for **NIB**? _____
10. What is the code for **WET**? _____
11. What does the code **728** mean? _____

■ Read the following information. Work out the answer. Write your answer on the line.

12. Luca lives in a block of flats. His flat is on the first floor. His neighbour, Frankie, lives in a flat two floors above him. On which floor does Frankie live? _____

End of test.

| Score: | Time taken: | Target met? |

Target time: **12 minutes**

If these words were listed in alphabetical order, which word would come **third**? Write the answer on the line.

Example dog   cat   vet   sit   cow   ____dog____

1. tin   pot   sow   rub   lid   _____

2. man   kit   dip   lie   bid   _____

3. rip   wit   and   bow   zoo   _____

4. ivy   jug   wet   can   pig   _____

Find the letter that completes each sentence. Use the alphabet to help you. Write the letter on the line.

A B C D E F G H I J K L M N O P Q R S T U V W X Y Z

Example **A** is to **B** as **D** is to ___E__ .   (+1 each time)

5. **F** is to **E** as **S** is to _____ .

6. **B** is to **E** as **K** is to _____ .

7. **T** is to **Q** as **H** is to _____ .

8. **E** is to **G** as **W** is to _____ .

Use the information given to answer the sum. Write your answer as a **letter**.

Example A = 1   B = 2   C = 3   D = 5   **A + B =** ___C__   (1 + 2 = 3)

9. A = 34   B = 16   C = 30   D = 14   **C – B =** _____

10. A = 23   B = 12   C = 25   D = 35   **B + A =** _____

11. A = 19   B = 21   C = 11   D = 10   **D + C =** _____

Read the following information. Work out the answer. Write your answer on the line.

12. George paid 35p each for 2 lollies. How much did he pay altogether? _____

End of test.

Score:	Time taken:	Target met?

⬇
■ **Two** words in each sentence must change places so that the sentence makes sense. Underline the two words.

Example Where do you <u>to</u> <u>go</u> school?   (Where do you <u>go</u> <u>to</u> school?)

1. My mum flowers likes.
2. Fish in swim the sea.
3. The roared lion loudly.
4. Monkeys bananas eat.

■ Find the missing letter that completes **both** words. Write the letter on the line. Choose your answer from these letters:
l r e k n t

Example tap (_e_) at   (tape and eat)

5. dea (__) ike
6. kne (__) lf
7. roo (__) ile
8. lio (__) ext

■ Find the next letter in the sequence. Use the alphabet to help you. Write the letter on the line.

A B C D E F G H I J K L M N O P Q R S T U V W X Y Z

Example A B C D E ___F___   (+1 each time)

9. F E D C B ____
10. M N O P Q ____
11. V U T S R ____

■ Read the following information. Work out the answer. Write your answer on the line.

12. A man, a woman and a boy are in a bus queue. The boy gets onto the bus first, then the woman and finally the man. Who gets on the bus last? _____   End of test.

Score:		Time taken:		Target met?	

Target time: 12 minutes

◼ Use the information given to answer the sum. Write your answer as a **letter**.

Example A = 1   B = 2   C = 3   D = 5   **A + B =** __C__   (1 + 2 = 3)

1. A = 4   B = 6   C = 3   D = 18   **C × B =** _____

2. A = 20   B = 10   C = 2   D = 5   **A ÷ B =** _____

3. A = 9   B = 2   C = 6   D = 12   **B × C =** _____

4. A = 25   B = 5   C = 10   D = 4   **A ÷ B =** _____

◼ Find the code. Use the alphabet to help you. Write the code on the line.

A B C D E F G H I J K L M N O P Q R S T U V W X Y Z

Example If the code for **TOP** is **UPQ**, what is the code for **TIP**? __UJQ__ (+1 each time)

5. If the code for **RED** is **QDC**, what is the code for **COT**? _____

6. If the code for **COD** is **BNC**, what is the code for **DOT**? _____

7. If the code for **UP** is **TO**, what is the code for **LIE**? _____

◼ Underline the pair of words that mean almost the **same**.

Example (hot, cool)   (freezing, sunny)   (cool, cold)

8. (drink, lick)   (taste, flavour)   (buy, give)

9. (rock, stone)   (soft, sky)   (tree, beach)

10. (boat, ship)   (tea, fish)   (stick, stream)

11. (lift, hit)   (cry, smack)   (bite, nip)

◼ Read the following information. Work out the answer. Write your answer on the line.

12. There are 9 flowers in a vase. 3 are yellow, 2 are red and the rest are blue.
    How many blue flowers are there? _____

End of test.

Score:		Time taken:		Target met?	

⬇
■ Underline the two words, **one** from each group, that together make one new word. The word from the first group comes first.

> Example (<u>foot</u>, head, face)   (shoe, <u>ball</u>, mask)   (football)

1. (step, stair, climb)   (friend, mother, house)
2. (track, to, path)   (way, go, yes)
3. (tooth, mouth, smile)   (hair, brush, white)
4. (look, in, down)   (see, over, stairs)

■ Find the missing letter that completes **both** words. Write the letter on the line. Choose your answers from these letters:

g   n   t   r   e

> Example tap (_e_) at   (tape and eat)

5. ros (__) at
6. tow (__) ine
7. bi (__) ood
8. doo (__) oom

■ Find the **three-letter word** hidden in each longer word. You will not need to change the letter order. Underline the word and write it on the line.

> Example la<u>the</u>   <u>the</u>

9. great   _____
10. grinned   _____
11. dripped   _____

■ Read the following information. Work out the answer. Write your answer on the line.

12. Priya leaves school at 3.30 p.m. It takes her 15 minutes to get home. What time does she arrive home? _____

End of test.

Score:		Time taken:		Target met?	

Target time: **12 minutes**

Work out the missing number. Write it on the line.

Example 3 [5] 2   4 [6] 2   5 [__8__] 3
(a + b = ?, where a is the number on the left and b is the number on the right)

1. 21 [20] 1   23 [20] 3   26 [_____] 6
2. 22 [32] 10   17 [30] 13   35 [_____] 15
3. 3 [6] 2   4 [20] 5   3 [_____] 5
4. 14 [10] 4   15 [6] 9   20 [_____] 8

Underline the two words, **one** from each group, that are most **opposite** in meaning.

Example (large, down, in)   (tiny, tree, hat)

5. (kind, good, star)   (bad, great, cross)
6. (old, little, pot)   (fast, sister, young)
7. (bag, black, paint)   (white, snow, toe)
8. (fun, clown, happy)   (cry, sad, book)

Change the first word into the last word. Only change **one** letter at a time. You must make a new word in the middle. Write the new word on the line.

Example MAN [___PAN___] PIN

9. WIN [_____] JIG
10. LOW [_____] DOG
11. LIE [_____] TIN

Circle the letter next to the **true** statement.

12.   Apes like to eat fruit. Monkeys are a type of ape.

If the above statements are true, which one of the following statements must also be true?
A. All fruit is healthy.
B. Monkeys like to eat fruit.
C. Monkeys have tails.

End of test.

Score:		Time taken:		Target met?	

⬇
■ Make a new word. Change the third pair of words in the same way as the other pairs. Write the new word on the line.

> Example (mat, at)   (fit, it)   (son, ___on___)   (take away the first letter of the first word

1. (bug, dug)   (bin, din)   (bay, _____)
2. (plane, plan)   (twine, twin)   (slime, _____)
3. (mood, mod)   (soon, son)   (loop, _____)
4. (old, gold)   (ill, gill)   (all, _____)

■ Underline the word that goes best with the three words in brackets.

> Example (bonnet, cap, beanie)   <u>hat</u>, coat, shoes

5. (tiger, lion, leopard)   cheetah, elephant, seal
6. (elf, pixie, gnome)   fairy, giant, castle
7. (mug, glass, beaker)   plate, cup, tree
8. (jump, skip, hop)   sleep, cry, run

■ Choose the word in brackets that will complete the sentence in the best way. Underline the answer.

> Example **Cat** is to **kitten** as **dog** is to (paw, <u>puppy</u>, animal).

9. **Pull** is to **push** as **up** is to (door, out, down).
10. **Strawberry** is to **red** as **lemon** is to (purple, blue, yellow).
11. **Write** is to **pen** as **play** is to (toy, spoon, shoe).

■ Read the following information. Work out the answer. Write your answer on the line.

12. Lucy has a collection of 6 teddy bears. Half are brown, 2 are black and 1 is pink. How many are brown? _____

End of test.

Score: _____   Time taken: _____   Target met? _____

Target time: **12 minutes**

Find the letter that completes each sentence. Use the alphabet to help you. Write the letter on the line.

A B C D E F G H I J K L M N O P Q R S T U V W X Y Z

Example **A** is to **B** as **D** is to __E__ .   (+1 each time)

1. **P** is to **M** as **V** is to _____ .

2. **A** is to **C** as **U** is to _____ .

3. **Z** is to **W** as **I** is to _____ .

4. **P** is to **S** as **D** is to _____ .

In each group, three words go together and one is the odd one out. Underline the word that does **not** go with the other three.

Example one   two   <u>out</u>   six

5. rain   snow   sun   night

6. soft   silky   short   smooth

7. cold   freezing   icy   wet

8. pen   bag   pencil   crayon

Find the next letter in the sequence. Use the alphabet to help you. Write the letter on the line.

A B C D E F G H I J K L M N O P Q R S T U V W X Y Z

Example A B C D E __F__   (+1) each time

9. A C E G I ____

10. L N P R T ____

11. F I L O R ____

Read the following information. Work out the answer. Write your answer on the line.

12. Freddie paid £2 each for some toy cars. He bought 3 cars.
How much did he pay altogether? _____

End of test.

Score:		Time taken:		Target met?	

■ Choose the word in brackets that will complete the sentence in the best way. Underline the answer.

> Example **Cat** is to **kitten** as **dog** is to (paw, <u>puppy</u>, animal).

1. **Clean** is to **dirty** as **tidy** is to (messy, lost, fresh).
2. **Red** is to **cherry** as **yellow** is to (apple, pea, banana).
3. **Roar** is to **lion** as **bark** is to (horse, dog, fish).
4. **Octopus** is to **sea** as **frog** is to (house, hutch, pond).

■ Find the next number or symbol in the sequence. Write it on the line.

> Example 14 15 16 17 18 __19__ (+1 each time)

5. 99 98 97 96 _____ 94

6. ☺ ☹ ☺ _____ ☺

7. £ $! £ $! _____

8. 60 55 50 45 _____

■ The word in square brackets has been made by some of the letters from the two outside words. Make a new word in the middle of the second group of words in the same way. Write the new word on the line.

> Example (toe [tap] rap)   (low [__lit__] s<u>it</u>)

9. (lap [lad] dim)   (won [_____] wed)
10. (tow [tea] ear)   (dip [_____] ogre)
11. (see [star] tar)   (we [_____] hen)

■ Read the following information. Work out the answer. Write your answer on the line.

12. Lulu will be 7 on her next birthday. How old is she now? _____

End of test.

Score:	Time taken:	Target met?

Target time: **12 minutes**

■ Find the missing number in each equation. Write it on the line.

Example 1 + 3 = 2 + ___2___   (1 + 3 = 4 and so does 2 + 2)

1. 20 − 3 = 14 + _____

2. 14 − 7 = 5 + _____

3. 10 × 2 = 15 + _____

4. 50 ÷ 10 = 3 + _____

■ Match the number codes to the words. Use this to help you work out the answers to the questions. Write your answers on the lines.

PET   PAT   ALL   732   712   355

5. What is the code for **TEA**? _____

6. What is the code for **LET**? _____

7. What does the code **735** mean? _____

■ Underline the pair of words that are most **opposite** in meaning.

Example (big, small)   (down, round)   (elephant, house)

8. (push, pull)   (pat, cook)   (shut, close)

9. (dress, brother)   (boy, girl)   (hair, sock)

10. (real, stuck)   (easy, hard)   (very, maybe)

11. (light, me)   (button, letter)   (on, off)

■ Circle the letter next to the **true** statement.

12.   A daisy is a type of flower. All flowers have a stem.

      If the above statements are true, which one of the following statements must also be true?
      A. Daisies are pretty.
      B. Daisies have a stem.
      C. All daisies are white.

End of test.

Score: _____   Time taken: _____   Target met? _____

Schofield&Sims

the long-established educational publisher specialising in maths, English and science

Verbal Reasoning 1 is a collection of short, language-based problem solving tests. Each timed test includes age-appropriate questions, providing opportunities for children to practise and master verbal reasoning skills in preparation for the 11+ and other school selection tests. The first of six verbal reasoning books in the **Rapid Reasoning Tests** series, this book covers the following question types: word and letter patterns; vocabulary; spelling; number patterns and problem solving.

Rapid Reasoning Tests provides short, effective, timed tests in reasoning. The series comprises six books of verbal reasoning tests and six books of non-verbal reasoning tests.

Written by experienced teachers and designed for independent use, **Rapid Reasoning Tests** has been carefully structured to provide practice of key, standard format question types. Each collection of tests has been designed for use over one year and provides one section per term in order to support regular practice.

Key features

- **Short tests** requiring few resources that are easy to fit into a busy timetable.
- A **target time** for each test encourages children to work quickly and develop the necessary exam skills for success in the 11+ and other tests.
- **Pull-out answers** in the centre of each book can be easily removed.
- **Free downloads** to support the series are available from the Schofield & Sims website.

The full series includes the following books:

Verbal Reasoning 1	978 07217 1238 3	**Non-verbal Reasoning 1**	978 07217 1226 0	**(Ages 6–7)**
Verbal Reasoning 2	978 07217 1239 0	**Non-verbal Reasoning 2**	978 07217 1227 7	**(Ages 7–8)**
Verbal Reasoning 3	978 07217 1313 7	**Non-verbal Reasoning 3**	978 07217 1228 4	**(Ages 8–9)**
Verbal Reasoning 4	978 07217 1241 3	**Non-verbal Reasoning 4**	978 07217 1229 1	**(Ages 9–10)**
Verbal Reasoning 5	978 07217 1242 0	**Non-verbal Reasoning 5**	978 07217 1230 7	**(Ages 10–11)**
Verbal Reasoning 6	978 07217 1243 7	**Non-verbal Reasoning 6**	978 07217 1231 4	**(Ages 11–12)**

MIX
From responsible sources
FSC® C110589
www.fsc.org

ISBN 978-07217-1238-3

9 780721 712383

ISBN 978 07217 1238 3
Key Stage 1
Age range 6–7
£3.95
(Retail price)

For further information and to place an order visit
www.schofieldandsims.co.uk or telephone 01484 607080